DEMISE
OF
CANE FIELD
PARADISE

Georgia Brown

HANSIB

First published in 2022 by Hansib Publications
76 High Street, Hertford, SG14 3TA, UK

info@hansibpublications.com
www.hansibpublications.com

ISBN 978-1-912662-73-9
ISBN 978-1-912662-74-6 (Kindle)
ISBN 978-1-912662-75-3 (ePub)

Printed in Great Britain

DEDICATION

In honour of, and gratitude to, my beloved
grandparents, Reginald and Isolyn Tyne;

For Zero, my first pure love;

Dr Trevor Munroe, you are loyal to the black,
gold and green;

For the people that have called Duckenfield home,
we have lived and cherished 'The good ole days'.

"A people without the knowledge of their past history, origin and culture is like a tree without roots."

Marcus M. Garvey

PREFACE

The green, countryside village of Cane Field Paradise is nestled near Morant Point in the eastern-most parish of St Thomas in Jamaica. The inhabitants were a mixture: like everything else, they were different among themselves in terms of age, intelligence, skills and experiences. They were immensely adept at handicrafts and were talented tradesmen and farmers. The men shared similar physical characteristics: muscular calves, sculpted arms, and protruding bellies.

The residents were energetic and they had a great love of music. They were happy, dancing people and spent plenty of time with each other. The elders were eager to engage in polite philosophical conversations, and the children were an integral part of the delightful bunch. At every given opportunity, they formed a coterie and played together.

On one hand, the residents lived their lives with an unquestionable virtue: faith in God and hope for Parousia. But on the other, their lives were not as conspicuous as it appeared, and among them were believers in God and superstitions. Obeah and myth had been cultivated in their consciousness. Even while at work, a cleansing of the mind and body were necessary to overcome their restless spirit.

Jobs at the colonial sugar estate were guaranteed to any able-bodied person. The nine-decades-old sugar factory was more than a building. It narrated an account of the residents, neighbouring communities, roads, rivers and dams. The people were acutely aware of their asset and the extent to which it influenced their daily lives. The sheer determination to work was the nexus between pride and dignity. They wanted the necessities of life, but they also wanted to enjoy life.

On payday, the verdant cane field village was just as vibrant as in the big city, but the merriment and excitement of the moment were often out of the ordinary – drunkenness, obscenity, greed, jealousy, duping, and jail-time!

Newcomers learned not to disrupt the cultural climate. Cane Field Paradise was noted for its civility and good-natured people, and respect and brotherhood were afforded to all. It was a feeling that was contagious, like the scent of the sweet rum which flowed like water. Rum was the staple of goodness that marked the perpetual phase in the history of the village.

Today, the village is a far-cry from the 'paradise' it once was. It is with hope that this vision of days gone by serves to examine the past, illuminate the present and determine the future. For in all good grace, the village and its legacy must be preserved for posterity.

Georgia Brown

1

The shimmery grandeur of the morning sun lit the verdant commons of Cane Field Paradise. The ingress to the enclosed village is off the Golden Grove main road, on a one way in and out straight, narrow, bumpy road, with deviations of lanes and avenues that were named after famous settlers. Cane fields encircle and cut through the village, while hemming Blue Mountain, palm trees and flowering plants captured the steady flow of the east-end breeze and harmonised the glide between twittering birds and clicking butterflies. The generosity of Mother Nature was conducive to the small, thriving, cultivated, antique sugar village. Luminant streams, spanned by short bridges, were abundant with jangas.[1] Trees were always laden with fruits and vegetables and the people had enough wholesome and nourishing food to eat.

Meal times were communal, whether cooking commercial or domestic, the villagers fed each other. Mobile food carts and food joints, with music, were located at every visible nook in the cane fields and along the factory road and at all entrances of the factory. Their diets mainly consisted of large portions of starchy ground provisions,

---

1. Jangas – freshwater crayfish.

meat, seafood and poultry. The longevity of the inhabitants was more than three score years and ten.

The village was not just beautified with landscape; the greatest allure was its people. It was a peaceful coexistence of family, friendship and felicity. Their way of life almost seemed perfect. They appreciated the simple pleasures of life, which were considered luxuries to them: the fair weather, the comradery, and the cane fields. A joint of cane was a great commodity and the people were wealthy in sugar and spirit.

Living in the village was a desiring experience. Activities were effortlessly mundane. The men making their way to work, depending on the time of the day, would stop and have a shot of spirit. The elite men gathered under an ackee tree to play dominoes, Ludo or crown and anchor. The Indian barber had men and boys waiting for the next haircut. Basi, who never had a job, sat on a landing all day and wrote numbers on a piece of cardboard box. Ms Sadling collected pig feed every evening from the lady next door. Mr Spice passed by morning and evening at the exact time with his herd of cows and a long switch to lash the unruly ones. Pearly was always on the street begging for a hundred dollars, and an old man sat on the cracked shop piazza holding a stick, with his lips twisted to one side, repeating the same words: "Aah sah, cost of living is high!"

Within the village, character was a measure of social status and not wealth. The elders exemplified righteous ways of living. They lived virtuous and peaceful lives. They were the protectors and advocates of the village. Kindness and empathy were commonplace. Their respect and affection for each other was expressed in the mantra: "We are *naggos*." The word *naggos* and the word *born-yahs* had the same meaning. They were people of invariably descendants who were born and raised in the village, and most, if not all, were related. The natives were humble, yet understandably proud of their legacy. Most of them never journeyed outside of the village, and if they did, like birds, they flew back to their nest.

The village was a home to many. The populace grew exponentially during crop-season. Crop season is a symbol of bounty; it enticed people to the village like bees to pollen. Industrious and prideful transient workers came to the village for gainful employment at the booming sugar estate. Other peripatetic lives brought them there. Newcomers were welcomed with great enthusiasm, but character was of utmost importance. They were usually met by the village councillors and thoroughly interrogated; having made all the enquiries and once the briefing was over, they were allowed to remain. Other considerations for newcomers were at the discretion of the host. But while they were allowed to remain in the flawless rural village, they were subjected to abiding by the laws composed by the honourable natives. At the same time, newcomers were encouraged to establish righteous ways of living and strived to acquire all that was good. The natives were usually hospitable to them as well. They allowed them to dine at the sumptuous table and offered the *naggos'* cuisine: white rice, crab tomalley[2] and a toast of white rum.

Rum was an aspect of the village, so too was the 80ft colonial sugar factory and the 135ft chimney that rose atop its commons on the rising and falling layered cane fields. At nights, a spectrum of lights from the towering factory beamed throughout the village. Cane harvesting and cultivation heightened the rhythm of life. The factory operated around the clock. The sights, sounds and scenes that accompanied crop time awakened the village.

---

2. Crab tomalley – crab cooked with coconut milk, spices and herbs.

The *carchi* announced the starting and ending time of every shift. The long, drawn-out, deafening echoes of the *carchi* that transcended beyond distant villages could not go unnoticed. The area was filled with: the scent of the broiling sugar and sour smell of the rum canes; the trail of canes that fell off tractors and trailers; the sound of tractor engines revving against clutches; the hastening footsteps of people going to work; the sight of camouflaged rangers on the lookout for stray cattle; the melodic hums and tunes of cane-cutters in the field; the sight of white long-necked garlings jutting in the brown open fields in search of worm food; the gentle breeze from the swaying cane-leaves; the tapering tails of mongooses in and out of the cane fields; and the blending sounds of files scraping against machetes.

2

A section of the population of the estate's employees was ordinary people with ordinary intelligence and ordinary lives. They learned their trade, bettered themselves and kept their jobs; and with passing years, they were only discharged of their duties due to infirmities and pains. Working at the factory was like a mark of distinction. Before the sun rose over the cane fields and the dew fell off the grass, the workers were already on the move, and all were essential, from the headman to the field labourers.

Labouring in the cane fields in an often inauspicious condition was not that simple. It demanded intense labour and skills, but the workers mustered the courage for the arduous stooping, staggering and back-breaking task. The weather, for the most part, was unfaithful. They could not escape the heat of the sun, the blustering wind, the flashes of lightning, the descent of the rain. But despite the vicissitudes of the weather, humble, hardworking and possessed of strength and stamina, described the field labourers. Their manoeuvring was adaptive and impressive. In the thickest of the cane-vines and in what seemed like seconds, green or burnt canes were chopped and layered into heaps and tractors and trailers transported canes to the factory.

The women, in preparation for cane cultivation, were just as skilled; in preparation for the task, they disguised their heads with wraps beneath big broad hats, veiled their faces with handkerchiefs and layered their bodies with long undergarments to confront nature. Side by side, they weeded and manured the alluvial-rows of bedded fields. Their calculable hours were squarely supervised, but the workers used humour to help them quicken their work. Together they hummed, sang, whistled, chatted and laughed.

At the signal of each workday, same as last, days felt like weeks and weeks felt like months and months felt like years. On the long, widened, bending miles of limestone road, and for what seemed like an eternity, they journeyed. Many times, darkness preyed on the evening and the starry sky guided the night. Many times, raindrops were blended with teardrops. Their source of strength was each other, and no one was left behind. They held each other up like a stick on a clothesline. They never murmured or complained. They endured with humbleness. Their extraordinary faith in God and their indomitable spirit were their motivation. Their supplications and prayers were recited through their favourite endearment from the Book of Genesis: "By the sweat of thy brow, thou shall eat bread." But their hope was for their children to attain the skills, knowledge and tools necessary for a better life than theirs.

It was a tradition for the village children who became mature adults to tend to their parents in sickness and in old age. Their undertaking was culturally motivated. For the children knew from when they were young that the sins of their negligence would visit upon them. After all, their parents did all that they could in the best way they knew. Hunger was not felt among them and a roof was assured over their heads. Thereupon, the children were to accept the challenge and strive to supersede them, and to that extent it was worth it for the aged parents to enjoy the privilege, security and comfort in their golden years. A reminder of the children's obligation was reiterated through the indefatigable voice of singer Alton Ellis:

Children go out to school
Smarter than your father
Don't be a fool
Let the people be led
Take care of them instead

'Lord Deliver Us' Alton Ellis

obs at the estate were not in any form of nepotism or favouritism. The prospect of acquiring a job was contingent on one's potential. Varying age groups made up the labour force. Young fellows generally quit school to learn a trade; when they were done with training, employment was secured. Others juggled work and school. The estate's inestimable contribution was unmatched. It spearheaded year-round cultural enrichments: films, guided tours, sporting events, apprenticeships and traineeships. The residents believed themselves to be doing good, and they were plainly right about themselves. The estate had given them an opportunity to be economically independent and socially motivated.

Crop over was quite eventful at the factory. When the days were nearing and the last set of canes arrived and the last bulk of sugar broiled, employees felt an alleviating gratification similar to drinking rum, and at such a moment, a quickening, rhythmic effusive blast of the carchi marked the end of the crop over. It also served as an announcement for the 'blue-foots'[3]. The natives were in favour for the transient workers to leave the village and return afresh for the next crop season. At the same time,

3. Blue foots – people who were not born in the village and came from elsewhere mainly to work at the estate.

crop over was quite similar to Christmas; it was marked with merriment. Festive gathering of sumptuous food and drinks ended the usual productive year. The village Santas were also extremely generous, and the uncontained generosity of the spirit rested on everyone.

The factory men worked hard, but possessing a strong sense of duty did not rule out pleasure. They divided their time between work and play. At the end of June, after crop over, when the transient workers gathered their belongings and left, fidelity did not accompany them. Some had not put their pennies to good use. They had gambled all their farthings and left offspring and weeping mothers behind.

With no real jobs, mothers were burdened with many thoughts on supporting themselves. But not all the women's lives were profoundly affected in the same fashion. When the truth, the lies, and the half-truths were revealed, the men had to pay for their deception. Others created a subfamily, and the mistress became a trophy. At the same time, the women were seen as homewreckers, terrifying in such a way that the elderly natives had to intervene; for if they did not, marriages would be dissolved. It was that simple. Such was the way of life, so much so that, it had grown increasingly disturbing for wives when they discovered the astounding revelation of their spouses' secret love affairs and love children.

At the same time, trapping of money was common. The workers had to dig a little deeper in their pockets, because there were women in the village that were indifferent. They lived a complete life of idling, begging and conning. They would meet the men at the factory gate or wherever pay-outs were made. Others queued up at rum bars and food joints. The men treated them well. The women's ferocious appetite was often met with selections of food they desired, such as: curried goat and white rice, jerk chicken and festival or peppered greasy jerk pork with alcoholic beverages.

The men, sometimes, effortlessly got away with them. In every nook and cranny, a man was jammed up 'one away' with a woman and there was nothing left to chance. They looked odd, but their needs went beyond their egos. Marriage and age differences were not hindrances and there were not any known cases of statutory rapes; relationships were usually consensual. Some of the men were as old as time itself, but their hair was as black as coal. It was not difficult to guess their ages either; the black stained dye disappeared around the contours of their edges, and wrinkles protruded from the corners of their jawlines; their childish grins displayed synthetic teeth; their moustaches, beards and eyebrows were incompatible with the dye and spurted grey hairs like morning glories.

But the women would rather be an 'old man's pet than a young boy's slave'. Drunken men were blindly robbed. The women often bragged about how much money they had pocketed, how much food they had brought home and how many drinks they had. Other men fell prey to drunken assaults. The men who were mindful of swirling rumours paid for their impairment to keep hushed secrets. While the women bantered on how much money they had received, the men bantered about the broken promises they had made. But in the end, bargains were made, promises kept and deals negotiated.

The fortnightly pay days were heydays with the moon madness, intense excitement and the uncontrolled chaos. A floodgate of desperate vendors and destitute beggars came flocking through the streets. Seemingly unstoppable, they were numbered five times a score or five times a baker's dozen. They were of every age and appearance: old, young, fat, slim, ragged, mangled, paraplegic, blind, dumb, deaf, sane and insane. There were pregnant women and women with children clinging to their hips and backs. They crawled on hands and knees. They had come forth by drop-offs or walk-ins, by day and by night.

Testimonies of their expeditious journeys were alarming. It was like the Israelites crossing the Red Sea to reach the Promised Land. Or perhaps their hope of survival was within the village, and the words of the song reassured the pilgrims in the following lines:

> *Going to the Promised Land, oh gosh*
> *...*
> *There's plenty of land for you and I, by and by*
> *Lots of food to share for everyone*
> *No time for segregation in the promised land, oh gosh*
>
> 'Promised Land' Dennis Brown

Up and down the street, the vendors and beggars trotted. Even toddlers that could barely put two words together were used as props in the begging game. The residents were usually quite charitable and convivial. The beggars never returned the same way that they came; neither had anyone fainted from hunger or starvation. They fed the hungry and clothed the naked. They got enough food to eat, groceries to carry home and money to spend. The natives went by the mantra, "Give to the poor and needy and God will give you some more." The village prospered because of its benevolence and obligation to God's will – a common deed of rectitude: "Whoever is kind to the poor lends to the Lord, and He will reward them for what they have done." Now and then, an old anecdote resurfaced among the villagers: "Cane Field Paradise is a place that rescues the perishing and cares for the dying." No one in the village remained hungry during crop season. The people lived and abided by the affirmation of the frequently listened song:

Let the naked be clothed
Let the blind be led
Let the hungry be fed
And the aged be protected

'Lord Deliver Us' Alton Ellis

The street thronged with eager people; curious glances caused them to invariably bounce into each other, step on toes and knock each other to the ground. You were considered lucky to find an empty walkway. The street and store piazza were cordoned off with vehicles, boom boxes, stereos, and vendors' carts. Sights and scenes of vendors were everywhere, and there were more sellers than buyers. Children were a part of the selling and juggling; their pleading eyes and gullible voices were appealing, "Buy something from me today, nuh, nice lady." The competitiveness of bargains and sales was maddening.

Everything and anything was up for sale. All sorts of collectable junks were on display: used rakes, electric floor polishers, cutlasses, Walkmans, cassettes, flashlights, batteries, lamp-burners, figurines, toys, handkerchiefs and what seemed like home-made perfumes and nail polishes. Small portions of bleaching creams were also sold in bags for those who were not able to buy the entire tube and for those whose desire was to mix the substances for an effective change of their skin's colour, to become 'brownings'. At food stalls, there were smoky jerked chicken and pork grilling on half tin drum-pans; festivals in huge 'dutchies'[4] sizzling in cooking oil; large soup-pans on wood or coal fire; potato puddings, escoveitched fish and saltfish fritters and fry dumplings in glass cases, roasted peanuts in wheelbarrows and on bicycle bars. Just about everyone on the street had their hands and mouths occupied with food while the air busted with intoxicating beverages.

The energy all around was unmatched and infectious. The concurrence of events was such that dressmakers and tailors worked non-stop, altering and sewing clothes for the revellers. On the other hand, transportation in and out of the village was lined in readiness at any given hour. The factory roads were used as backstreets by the desperate and impatient meandering vehicle operators for making shorter routes, evading the traffic police and avoiding the deep potholes. However, during crop season, the roads were narrowed and choked. Heavily laden tractors and trucks were lined up one behind the other or next to each other with piles of canes mounted in the air that left trails of canes on the gravelly road.

---

4. Dutchie – thick iron cooking pot locally made in Jamaica.

...

I'm in a dancing mood

When you feel the beat
You've got to move your feet
You've got to clap your hands
You've got all the soul
Deep down inside
'Cause you can't hide

'Dancing Mood' Delroy Wilson

6

uildings trembled under the heavy vibrations from the sound systems, while the deafening music pounded the air. One sound system drowned out the next and the next. It was music-madness, but the people loved it. They danced from one sound system to another. The old fellows had a penchant for ska and rocksteady music of the 1960s. They also got the supple grooves: legs dropping, hips turning, arms swaying and heads bobbing while they danced. At nightfall, round two of the dance scene and fashion show began. They showed up and showed out dressed in their Friday best.

The women dressed the part like pageantry; they flaunted their femininity and seemed quite comfortable in their skin. In body-hugging tight mini apparels, voluptuous thighs, tummies and titties were on display. The outfits seemed pricey and matched right down to their open-toe shoes. Their jewellery was flashy and oversized. The chains were as large as those used to tie a cow and their hoop earrings were the size of bangles. Their long colourful hair extensions attached with glue, threads, and gels were glittery and shiny, while their facial contouring was immaculately shaped: angled peaked eyebrows, long sooty eyelashes, red blush cheek bones and thick glossy lips. They dabbed themselves in strong perfumes and shimmery powder.

Like their female counterparts, the men were fashionably put together. They were flamboyantly dressed like 'rude boys'. A felt hat was kotched on one side of their head; they were in button-down shirts, tailor-made corduroy suits, leather belts and 'gentlemen shoes',[5] polished and shined. A substantial amount of showy jewellery was also worn: rings, chains, bracelets, earrings, and anklets, while the smell of Old Spice cologne lingered on them.

The dance patrons cheered themselves along with liquors, brandishing a stout or a beer in both hands. The men bought liquor for the ladies and themselves; half-way between each drink, another round was served. The orders at the counter were placed non-stop. As the liquor shimmered in their heads, it was a 'dance moves showdown'. Back-to-back, shoulder-to-shoulder, belly-to-belly, they rubbed and dubbed, pumped and lapped each other. They pivoted on their head tops, skinned out their legs and shimmied on their backs. Not to be outdone, there was the 'Miss Dancehall Queen' in the midst. She shook her head so vigorously that her neck rotated like a yoyo as she gyrated to the tune of *Dutty Whine*. The sultry and vulgar dance moves caused a traffic jam at the crossroads while onlookers' jaws dropped open. But the events of the evening came as no surprise, as there was only one thing to do, and that was to have fun. There was no limit to their happiness; nothing dampened their spirit; they let themselves go. It was the norm of the social life: the unrestrained, feeling good hours and competitive spirits. It was the moment when the ordinary became the extraordinary.

---

5. Gentlemen shoe – dressed up shoe with laces or buckle fastening.

They were awake all night under the liquor and the music. They danced 'til they became soaking wet. The sun lit in their faces. And, like crabs in search of a hole, some scrambled to get home; others were too drunk to make it. Barefooted, dishevelled and disoriented, they rested on the piazza. Their state and appearance were a far cry of how they were hours before. The condition in which they were, it was for the good of those who had children that they be held in the care of the grandparents.

The electrified scenes were everywhere all through the night – from the rum bars, to the gambling joints and to the mini theatre. Patrons queued up at the show house from early to settle in a front row seat on the long benches. The seating capacity was around fifty, and the ticket sales were influenced by the pre-screening of international and local action and comedy films. The entrance fee to the theatre was modest and even the movie going hustlers capitalised on the sales of peanuts, Icy Mints[6] and oranges.

Many of the small shops usually remained open throughout the night, and businesses fared even better than usual. Shopkeepers were generous to give extended credits to credible customers, knowing that their livelihoods were dependent upon them. The Chiney man's wholesale grocery was also an important business for consumers and small vendors alike, since they were able to buy in bulk and pay later. Money was not a hindrance. No one struggled to keep things afloat, and no one was in competition; each operation was sufficient in itself and enjoyed their share of customers.

---

6. Icy Mints – green/bluish hard peppermint candy made in Jamaica.

Everywhere and everything was accessible. Shops were positioned in a semicircle before and behind each other at the Crossroads; shelves were always stocked with household and food items. Of all the delectable spots, there was none like the acclaimed Circle D Bakery. The location on which it stood was in the centre of the spotlight. The bakery was one of its kind. Its oval shaped sign accentuated the primary and secondary colours of light and gave the village a magnificent twinkling night view. It served traditional pastries of bread, bulla, coco-bread, bread pudding and the succulent, savoury beef patties. Customers journeyed from near and far to indulge in the never before tasted mouth-watering, delightful, wholesome treats. As for the village children, the bakery was like an edible amusement park. They leapt into joy and their little faces glowed with guilt-free gladness and gratitude when savouring the dainty treats of sweetness.

onsidering rum as a happy medium, rum drinking became a way of life. The commoners as well as the nobles drank, as it was available in sufficient quantities. The aroma of broiling cane juice that reached the nostrils was as good as one could get. But in spite of the sniffing and over-powering vapour of the sweet rum scent, the factory did not brew rum. The people always had a good many drinks and often became addicted. In fact, the white rum was so strong that sometimes one gulp of undiluted shot and they were already drunk. The grocers' added incentive was through the sale of rum. At the dawn of day, the side windows of the shops were opened and rum drinkers would already be lining up. The bouts of drinking escalated on paydays and the atmosphere of drunkenness remained constant throughout. Believing that rum offered the solution to their troubles, they drank it unreservedly to bury their woes and worries. But, the causation of the rum often switched mood, emboldened mood and mellowed mood.

The spotlight was always on a rum bar near the crossroads. They toasted and drank with good cheers: handshaking, fist bumping and bear hugging each other. But in moments of drinking and chatting, and the rum swirling in their heads, they became loud, lewd and aggressive. They bantered and badmouthed each other. The insults were as damaging as a raging fire. Whenever they got into a fight, 'all hell would break loose'. It was like watching a group of overgrown kindergarteners; they were wild and restless. Everyone threw wild punches in the air and no one received a blow. And as drunk as they were, they never let go of their liquors. Their elaborate drinking and temper flare-ups caused some bartenders to limit the amount of liquor they could buy or they were ousted from the bar, but even in their drunkenness, they were acutely aware of an insult.

The saying, "Tom drunk but Tom nuh fool", gave meaning to the same proverb: 'A wise man can play a fool's role, but a foolish man cannot play wise.' Unsteady as they were on their feet, they still managed to move on to another location where the drinking would continue. Not all the bartenders were bothered by the uproars of the inebriated patrons because they were great tipsters and gratuity made up their salaries. And the men not only made copious spending on liquors, but they also had a voracious appetite for the salty red herrings, greasy peppered jerk pork and shrimps that were sold in the bars.

> *When you come here*
> *What you see here*
> *What you do here*
> *What you hear here*
> *When you leave here*
> *Let it stay here or*
> *Don't come back here*

Eyes raced with enthusiasm reading the bar sign's declaration: 'No reproof.' The affirmation was all that was needed. There were no moral codes; worse yet, the village bars were notorious for misplaced outrage and served as a refuge for avengers. Patrons publicised their troubles as they smoked and drank and spoke freely. Under the influence of the rum, and knowingly not cowed, nothing which was said could be held against them. Simply, they were not the object of their feelings, thinking, believing, doing or saying.

Another aspect of the bar life was the calendar of women almost bare of clothing plastered on the walls; serving as a provocative distraction, the pictures and the rum filled the drunkards' heads with imagination, bravery and distorted facts. And, if the painstaking cursing and drunken rages among them were not enough, they also blurted out racy comments that often insulted women. As much as they were drunk, there was too much within them that they had to unleash. The drunkards' behaviours were condoned in the lyrics of the song by the Mighty Sparrow:[7] 'Drunk and Disorderly'. And for those affirmations children were not allowed to be seen near bars.

---

7. Mighty Sparrow – Trinidadian calypsonian, songwriter and musician.

The energy level all around was dynamic. Others in the village were just as opinionated, but they had no host. It was a division of two worlds: one set happy in their rum spirit, and the other happy with salvation. The drunkards made their debut on the street. The scene was quite peculiar and inexplicable, with even mad men being drunk. With swift movements, they elbowed their way through the crowds. The maddening maniacs blasphemed, threatened and condemned both God and man. Their rants were inclined towards the exceptional and exciting events on paydays, but entertainment of this sort was not pleasing to the ageing *born-yahs*.

Still, the people were unconcerned about their telling. But in all truthfulness, sweet rum, dispensable cash and good humour marked the richness of the village life.

Madness, madness
They call it madness
...
I'm about to explain
That someone is losing his brain
Madness, madness
They call it gladness

'Madness' Prince Buster

There was a middle aged madame dressed in a 'colour-blinding', 'bees-catching', 'floor-sweeping' dress, with head tightly wrapped in a heavy matching cloth. She made an exit from the bar with a Bible held in her hands. Then, she began with an endless and uninteresting prayer followed by loud singing on top of her voice, "Stand up and tell me if you love my Jesus; Stand up and tell me if you love my Lord; I want to know if you love my Jesus. I want to know if you love my Lord."

Up and down, the madame paced the street, uttering words of prophecy: "Doomsday for the unrighteous!" The dreadfulness in her voice shifted from moans, to groans, to cursing and swearing. She spoke with no sense of righteousness; she cursed man for creating sins and called on the Prophet Elijah and the Angel Gabriel to convert and condemn sinners. Unlike the other proselytisers, people looked past her. Her words were meaningless and contrary when the rum diffused in her head. When done on the street, she returned to the bar where it all started, then held a dance-off show down. The madame was unbeaten in foot movements and waist-turning as she danced to the beat of reggae rock-steady.

Of all there was, none was like an overweight little man with a patent bushy beard and haggard steel looking hair; he stooped from the tides of ageing, the lack of care and the abuse of alcohol. He promenaded the street in ill-fitting trousers draped to his chest, handkerchief tied around his three-quarters sleeve shirt and a pair of sandals on his feet revealing claw-like toenails. To garner the attention of others, he held a megaphone and a flask of overproof rum to his mouth. But always, before he began, he would look at his wristwatch to ascertain the time, shuddered his shoulders and sipped on his liquor. A deep furrow appeared on his face when he beamed from a frown into a smile, then to a pensive expression, as though he was listening to an inner rambling voice. His eccentricity reminded the village children of the poem, 'Zachariah Zed'. Upon seeing him, they chanted:

Zachariah Zed, Zachariah Zed
Saw a big dumpling in his bed.
He started to eat, but it stuck in his teeth
So they called him Zachariah Dumpling Head.
'Zachariah Zed'

And another. With the moon out and the rum in, it was his habit to pick fights in his drunken stupor. The thunderously heavy-voiced deranged drinker held the villagers into giggles when he teased and taunted women. Prancing and pacing up and down the street like a raging bull, he carried a symbolic object aiming to lock away promiscuous women's reproductive parts. But before he became ill, he was among the worthy, a native, a responsible citizen, a family man and a competent worker. His jealousy and mistrust had cost him his well-paying ideal job. Rumours swayed that he had been 'obeahed', but given as they said, it seemed probable. The raucous laughter and the attacking of people were not indicative of his character, but the truth was, his job was a test of endurance and he broke under the pressure. He drenched his superiors with endless menacing and abusive words, ripping them with different 'colourful' descriptions. Without any contemplation, he was fired on the spot. Seeing the faces of his angry wife and nagging children, rum became the un-prescribed solution to his worries.

And another. In the better part of his heyday, he was above all things, calm by nature, and exhibited proper principles. He had lived a life of fulfilment. Born and raised in the village but never dated a villager. His wife was from Somalia – a country in east Africa. She was admirably beautiful with distinctive Indian features and traits: long, black, thin, flowing hair with an added flower, high cheekbones with applied rouge, straight nose with a ring in it, epicanthic eyes with eye shadows, thin lips with red lipstick, and her unrepentant smile highlighted a gold crown. The observation from nosy villagers stated that the wife was many years younger than he, but the couples' life was going well until misfortune beset. The woman ran off with the 'yard boy' and left the poor man in misery.

Women and alcohol had since become his best companions. The escorting of women and alcohol to his home was like the operation of a brothel. Riotous and querulous women confronted each other in brawls and fights and emotionally blackmailed each other, but he saw them as necessary evils; unfettered by anyone; loyal to none. Months after his house confinement, he looked like he had been through the 'valley of the shadow of death'. His eyeballs sunk in his head, his hair was quite grey, and his body was old and frail. His looks were not a measure of his strength; like a circuit preacher, he went out and about villages condemning women for creating sin.

And another. The arrogance within him could not be separated from self. His behaviour was an inferior lapse from his manly responsibilities. He gambled his fortnightly farthings on cards, numbers and horse. The man never drank, but in lieu of drinking, he dabbed the rum on his clothes and over his body. The strong smell of rum was an indication that he was drunk, but it was only a bluff! In the middle of the street, he took random steps to secure the landing of his feet, and nearing his home, he cursed like a sailor. The fearful and fretful wife watched him with contempt and remorse in her heart. The discourtesy was a slap in the face, but the deceiving husband never seemed fazed.

And another. He was charismatic, complex and cocky all at the same time, with an odd side to him. Rum put him in bad humour. He had an indescribably loose tongue and became comically frightening when he was drunk; he took to the streets and cursed like a sailor. When he was sober, he was the man whom everyone referred to as the best of the best. He was the only known barber in the village. Men and boys stood in line waiting for haircuts, but he was extremely impatient dealing with children. He had a stuck routine for work and hygiene. His cutting packed dirt floor area under the ackee tree was swept daily. His working tools were his whole life. His scissors, comb, razors, along with water, was always neatly displayed on a table.

At the standpipe, he washed his face, brushed his teeth and combed his hair. Then, he dampened his hand in an old cheese tin containing water and slid back his thin, silvery highlighted hair that remained intact throughout. Back to his working post, he threw on a barber's overcoat. He never chatted while working, but he listened and remembered everything; he was a mental solver and an avid reader. People tried to make sense of his unusual squabble, but to others, it was not surprising. The man was never seen with a woman or related to anyone in the village. He occupied an abandoned old house atop the hill and cooked his meal on a wooden fire out in the open. Ironically, only scant information about him was revealed; not even his real name was known. They called him Arrow, a name which was simply a synonym for quarrelsome.

And another. The meanest and loudest of them. Every Saturday morning at around the same time, the hurling of insults was taken from his lodging to the streets. The woman's mouth was as filthy as a dirty rag and the man referred to as the father was no different. Gambling, drinking and cheating were his temptations. He, like many of the drunkards, never admitted to their downfalls, and his reluctance to 'man up' to his responsibilities created a rift in his family. Their behaviour, at times, was followed with an arrest by the police after the family ganged up and rained blows on him.

Of all the drunkards, by far the most noticeable of them was the eccentric odd couple, nicknamed Heckle & Jeckle. Rum had cheated them out of the best years of their lives. Two days out of every fortnight, their unbecoming way of living became a spectacle. They sat on the embankment, as drunk as drunk could be, with dribbling, slimy mouth and unwinking, fuming, fiery red eyes fixed at each other, while each made accusations of lacking fidelity. Their conduct reminded the villagers of the song, Seven Drunken Nights:

And as I went home on Friday night as drunk as drunk could be
I saw a head upon the bed where my old head should be
Well, I called me wife and I said to her, "Will you kindly tell to me"
"Who owns that head upon the bed where my old head should be?"

Ah, you're drunk, you're drunk
You silly old fellow, still you can not see
...

'Seven Drunken Nights' The Dubliners

The heightening of the ambience quieted on Sundays. There was not any form of gambling, drinking or swearing. Reverence graced the day. Sounds and tones of music and people were tuneful, classy and churchy. It was such a respect for tradition that Sunday worshipers considered it as the 'Lord's Day'. In the eventide, some of the villagers would partake in ministerial work, as well as, churches brought their devotional service to the village square, and it was a continuity of worship and praise. The day was religiously kept right back until night fall.

Sundays were also deemed as 'rice and peas day,' as it was usually the main staple in the diet. But, Sundays were like Christmas. It was a day of fine festive dining and family. From every household, the aroma of sweet meals permeated the air, and the partaking of a full course meal was served on a decorated table of linen and cutleries. In addition, the sick and shut-ins were visited and fed. The little children were titivated in their 'Sunday best' clothing while awaiting the arrival of the 'fudge man', who came riding on a bike and tooting his horn in a thematic sound interpreted as: 'Toot, toot! Here comes fudgy!'

Weekday activities were mundane; throughout the street, stray dogs fought for bones, deserted goats nuzzled on walls, idle juke boxes turned records, combustible engines polluted the air, bottle police lurked around the bars, untamed cats purred at each other, children scurried to school and adults went about their business with an unstoppable energy that was enlivened on weekends. In commuting to and from work, the men stopped and had a drink and a smoke, but they had limits and never overindulged or were inebriated on the job. On Mondays, the credit union was usually busy as most responsible estate employees were putting away dividends for 'rainy days'.

It was the village that nurtured a child from protection to valour, and dealt with the co-disciplining. Young people valued the wisdom of the elders. They were endowed with super knowledge and were highly revered and trusted. They were keen at reasoning and telling folktales. The elders were usually the praying grandparents, the guardian angels, and the glue that held the family and village together. They set examples and gave advice.

Children were exhorted by their grandparents about the importance of manners and telling the truth because of the fear and punishment of what God would do to an ill-mannered child and a lying tongue. The grandparents' judgement was reflective, ethical and theological.

Aside from their apocalyptic lectures, gestures were used as a communicative technique; a fierce and uncompromising stare when a child misbehaved, the behaviour signalled a, 'Wait till I get home' warning. If the child continues to ignore, forgiveness was otherwise meaningless. The grandparents would make them a public example on the spot. The phrase: "You must be seen but not heard," must have reverberated in every child's head, as it was often said by the grandparents. In fact, manners were cultured in the village.

A child's head was hung low in contempt when he or she had been scolded; it was done with perfect composure, no shrugging of shoulders or nodding of the head. A 'yes' or a 'no' would at all times precede a proper noun. In addition, children who were brought up in non-restorationist households had to know the Lord's Prayer, the Ten Commandments, the Twenty Third Psalm and the Catechism, as well as having a place of worship. Not only did the home help to mould and develop a child's life, the village schools helped to cultivate values as well. High standards were set and expected of the students. Patriotism, etiquette, literacy, divinity and physical activities were reinforced. The school day passed with lessons and prayers. Prayers and grace were recited daily. The students recited morning and evening prayers, and grace before and after lunch, clasping their hands and closing their eyes, a gesture of giving reverence to God.

With such an abundance of respect and 'brought-upsy', they became recipients of honours and awards. In fact, some of the most successful and ambitious persons within leadership roles were products of Cane Field Paradise; it produced scholars and champions, politicians and entrepreneurs, judges and barristers.

randparents were also not reticent in imposing guidelines and setting restrictions in courtships. In dating, the men often found someone outside of the village, but it was usually not that simple. Serious choices were imposed upon them which they had to obediently adhere to. They were noble heirs and if only by nothing else, they married the women that their parents and grandparents approved of. By all accounts, there was a subtle test in character; the woman had to first prove her worthiness marked with the presence of three dispositions: practicality, maturity, and rationality. Marriage was a sacred and sensitive subject for the elders; they were meticulous in their approach and maintained conservative values. The natives protected people and property. It was for the social good of the family that the soon to be daughters-in-law must also be decent, honest, and clean.

The act was like marrying a prince, but the native first born sons were treated as royals. Some of the women who could not tolerate the unnerving situation packed their things and went back to their hometowns, but others were passive, obedient, unresisting, steadfast and eager to prove themselves. Under close observation, acute speculation and the right circumstances, resolute approval was given to the man to marry the woman. The decision was never to be wavered. It was important for the men to wed the women who exhibited a sameness in character of their grandmothers and mothers, because if nothing else, their names were of great importance; surnames asserted the dignity and respectability of a family and were used as collaterals.

Nicknames, on the other hand, were commonplace in the village. People were named in allusion to their looks, work, or actions, and the names remained with them for life. Proper names were also like novelties for children entering primary schools. Grandparents' tones and emphasis on syllables almost seemed difficult for the children to otherwise pronounce or spell accurately. As a matter of fact, Lloyd was interpreted as 'Llayd', and sometimes with an added 'ed' depending on the accented letter, 'Llayed'.

In another aspect of village life, businesses were never called by their registered names; they were often abbreviated or even called entirely by a different name. For example, the factory was nicknamed the 'Giddeon', while other places of business, with no official signs or marks on them, were called by the owners' name. Curiously, most Chinese-owned grocers were called either Ms Chin or Mr Chin.

13

he natives took extreme precautions to maintain a peaceful and measured society. People walked the streets freely without fear. Safety was the concern of everyone, and each had a share of responsibility in taking care of the other. Community policing was carried out on bikes and on foot. The honourable natives were of diverse groups and held positions as deacons, wardens, lay preachers and justice of the peace. They appointed themselves as police, presiding judge and jurors. They made provisional arrests, tried, and convicted wrongdoers. But it was necessary for the offenders to be brought before the counsellors, rather than the counsellors hunted for them. All trials and public hearings were conducted under the ackee tree in a location known as Lime-Skin Bump.

In adjudging criminals' actions, charges were taken into consideration. Each offence carried its own punishment. At the same time, the accused who came before the legislative body were not to defend themselves but to show contrition. Before the verdict was read, the arbitrators of the law discussed the prospect of the offenders and made them accountable based on the nature of their crimes. Crimes of any sort were not justifiable, and no one escaped the penalty or punishment of their actions. Stealing was a crime of laziness, an offence that was harshly dealt with categorically, as was a case of rape. Stealing and raping were deemed as acts committed through premeditation of lust, anger, and envy. There was no compromising or rationalising for such depravity. There was no recounting or recanting. There was no plea bargaining. There was no time to negotiate between accuracy versus truth. Deeds could not be undone. The idea that a man had stalked and molested an elderly woman angered the residents. While their fears and worries mounted, they were yet eager and anxious to hold the criminal accountable in an unorthodox martyrdom.

Newcomers, who committed crimes, were ingloriously ostracised. A thief stole a pair of socks and wore the evidence. The victim alerted the angry residents who intercepted and battered the helpless culprit. This, too, was the first case of a public flogging. Locals who broke the law would receive a lengthy tongue lashing and lecture in proverbial and scriptural lessons. The verdict was hammered with so much austerity that no one would have the proclivity for repeated wrong-doings. No one wanted the disgrace or the scourge of one's tongue on their family. In the old adage, it is said, "The tongue is sharper than the sword." To be desired in the village was a great honour; as a result, there were more heroes than villains.

ocial gatherings were commonplace. It did not matter the time, the residents remained calm and unhurried. The elders were resolute in giving advice and stating their opinions. Their responses were well thought out, and were sometimes followed by a groan and a short phrase, *'Aah sah.'* No one passed each other without a cheerful salutation: a nod, hug or a handshake, that immediately generated into lengthy chatter and laughter. Out of cultural politeness, the locals greeted each other as cousins and the younger folks greeted the elderlies as mothers, aunties or uncles. It was quite noticeable among the conversationalists that their words were always profound in bidding farewell: "God go with you," "God bless you, me child," "Walk good," or "Take care."

Aside from the court hearings, the elite men's society congregated under the notorious ackee tree. A long, rectangular wooden two-legged bench was attached to the tree, and where there was enough room, some would sit and others would stand. They remained there for long hours. They played games, listened to music and talked about events. They were great storytellers; they told unrelenting stories with far-off truths. The men were avid cricket fans. When it was test cricket and one day matches, they were completely attuned. On their persons, radios clung unobtrusively to their ears with modulated voices of cricket commentators and sounds of the players. The men listened with emotional zeal until the players were at break. Then, they would begin to clamour and curse at players who made a 'duck' or 'got run out'.

Within the circle, the elite gentlemen had multiple personalities and butted heads easily, but with the exception of one gentleman who was a man of respectable years. He was wrinkle free, bald headed and handsome. Always, he wore a pearly white 'bush jacket'[8] ironed and starched, and perhaps had many of the same colour. His pants were in the same order, belted and zipped with razor-sharp vertical pleats. His shoes were shined and clean. He was interested in cricket and the weather. Yet, he was less aggressive and talkative, but when he did on repeated terms, it was the same narrative that was old as time. It was about his experiences in Cuba and Panama. The men always listened attentively as if it was the first time they were being told.

The 'all self-important' rebutter among the group bore a striking resemblance to the caricature version of Popeye. He had a long chin, overgrown fingers and tiny structure. Fitting clothes for him seemingly had to be custom-made. He was always draped in oversized shirts and pants, with a huge sailor hat kotched on his small head and with a cigar in his large mouth. He was not very well liked. He knew what was wrong with everyone except himself. His mouth was ruthless, unfiltered and undiluted. His temper plummeted like manna from the sky. Yet, it did not matter how divided the gentlemen had been in an argument, an outsider could not intervene and take sides. The natives

---

8. Bush jacket – men's summer shirt. Known as a guayabera or Yucatan shirt in Spanish-speaking countries, but which Jamaicans call a 'bush jacket'. It was made popular in Jamaica by the country's charismatic Prime Minister, Michael Manley.

were forthright in letting you know it was not permissible, for they were family. Family and friendship were the source of strength the villagers needed to survive. Their bond could not otherwise be quantifiable. They had a genuine tolerant affection for each other.

15

There used to be a composed club house called Colour Red, where all the mature young adults intermingled with a show of strong affection and pleasant intimacy. The 'clubites' differed in age but had similar interests. A few of the old fellows took active roles in sharing their great sportsmanship experience with them. The strong, muscular, handsome young fellows often played football among themselves at Orange Walk or on the field in front of the factory. Both venues belonged to the estate. However, when they played competitive sports against other teams from neighbouring villages, there were usually roars of elation and an aura of pride when the cool and dapper fellows ran onto the ball-field. The fellows were skilful and talented and as fit as a fiddle. They almost always won every match that they played and brought home the trophy. The nimble-handed young ladies were just as unified on the netball court. They played against many good teams, but they prided themselves to be among the best and won all their games by large margins.

Another group of young fellows, whose interest was in music, formed their own coterie. They mainly congregated at a pub in the village called Alcove. They built speaker boxes, sound systems, spun records, dubbed or deejayed on sound tracks and added their own renditions. The impulsive, competitive, unrestrained, talented and gifted young fellows were unique in their delivery. Each endeavoured to outdo the other in an exchange of clean cultural lyrics and each was given a stage name fitting to his talent.

16

Like bees from a disturbed hive, the happy-go-lucky, ingenuous children shared the same buzz of enthusiasm when they met each other on the street. Their tiny legs and bare feet ran errands, but still, they used every opportunity to play. It did not take long for groups to be formed. The noisy bunch yelled and screamed, enjoying every aspect of their innocent zeal. They played and moved to other friends, then to another, then to another place. They did not have much, except plenty of time for each other.

The extent to which the children played often led to scratches, bruises, dirt, grime, and sweat all over their bodies. They played so rigorously that their patched clothes were torn apart. They never seemed exhausted; they played at length until their stomachs growled with hunger and the night fell in the evening. Their way of life was good times. They were free of worries, free of pain, free of sickness and free of guilt. And while they played, their spirits were competitive. They vied to outdo each other and tempers flared in the process, but as often as it occurred, they made-up with each other by the end of the day.

While the children strengthened their physical and mental wellbeing by playing, they played games according to the season. Most young lads took a keen interest in cricket. The older men were their mentors. But there were other village children whom their parents did not allow to go out of sight, so they played in their yards. They were seen doing somersaults or hula hoops or playing doll house, hopscotch or jacks.

When the girls were not at play, they were indoors studying their books or doing house chores. Their parents had meaningful conversations with them about the facts of life. They were informed about the birds and the bees and butterflies.

All the children had a balanced life. Education was valued in the households and the children fulfilled the expectations their parents had impressed upon them. The diligent and 'brainy' children received straight As and Bs in school. At such a young age, they recognised what they wanted to be in the future; they gradually became mature and intelligent adults and lived a fabulous life.

17

In health, sickness or death, the residents rallied around each other. They showed every mark of respect for the dead. A death announcement was first done with the pealing of the church bell, since most of the natives were Anglicans. Then out of community spirit, everyone did what was obligatory. They rallied around the family of the deceased. The days before the funeral, grave diggers moved swiftly with shovels and spades. Not a penny was charged, except family members brought them food and white rum.

Funerals were like concerts. A grand celebration befitting a noble sent off the dead. On the return of the body to the village in the hearse, solemn songs would be played, such as *One Glad Morning, When This Life is Over* or *Bringing In the Sheaves.* Then the procession, the theatrics, the band. People played flute, trumpets, tambourines and all the other instruments thereof. An array of beautiful flowers was mounted on caskets, hearse and graves. From the church to the grave side, the fanfare of farewell songs such as, *When We All Get to Heaven, Shall We Gather at the River, I Will Fly Away* and *I Am Going Home on the Morning Train* were sung.

Dead yard set-ups were the same. It involved prayer meetings, refreshments, and entertainment, all through the night. People played dominoes and cards. They told duppy stories. They ate, danced and sang. Dissonant voices rose in crescendo to varying catchy dead yard songs: *A Cum Me Just a Cum and mi Nuh Waan Nuh Boderation Oh!*

Kumina – drumming and dancing were an added entertainment, but only to those whose family members desired it. Kumina is an ancestral ceremonial practice, and can become quite fearsome and wild when participants' bodies were in alliance with a different energy and spirit. The participants would fall into a fitful rage, their bodies convulsing like an earthquake, their tongues protruding like dead animals and their eyes widening and turning like shake and wake dolls. The ground, the drum, and the trance had to be splattered with animal blood and rum to appease the 'encountering spirits'. And, if they had not done so, then the 'angry spirts' would enter them.

It was common for rum to be plentiful at dead yards and grave sites. It is a custom and tradition marked with superstitions. Rum splattered on the ground, around and about at dead yards and grave sites, served the same purpose of appeasing the spirts of the ancestors; even in death the naggos of the village were sacred and revered.

Heavy drinking was carried out in addition. Rum was free, and so, the people did not bother to sip. They drank it rapidly. The scent of rum would hang in the air and on their breaths, but that did not lessen the great trepidation attendees had departing from dead yards. As if someone was watching or listening, they made their departure in hurried silence, muted lips, and averted eyes; then like flocks of black birds, they walked home. They used flashlights and bottle torches[9] to illuminate their pathways.

---

9. Bottle torch – a long-necked glass bottle filled with kerosene with a piece of cloth inserted as a wick. When the wick is lit, the bottle-torch served as a portable lamp.

Upon reaching their houses, they would spin around three times before entering backwards. The gesture of spinning around three times was a probable cause that a supposing 'duppy' would not accompany them inside their homes, but the number three is an associated number of good and evil and given many meanings. For example, the number three in Chinese 'drop-hand' means dead. The village's Afro-natives told stories that ended the activities of the dead. And in theoretical term three means the 'Trinity'.

The residents had a love affair between superstition and Christianity. They went to the churches that offered a supernatural means of salvation. Their way of life was, superstition is to prophetic readers, as religion is to church. The reader man, the bush doctor, the medicine man, the obeah man, the prophet, the man with different aliases was never a native of the village, but he was the elder in charge of the church and its operations. Any outlet for healing and reading and revoking duppy were always flocked. Therefore, those church businesses thrived for good reasons.

Charged with superstition, the people led themselves in the paths of unrighteousness and darkness, for they were fearful and wanting in divination. When they found themselves in exceptional circumstances, they became timid, paranoid, cynical, idiotic, and insecure to the point that they would act upon their own illusions. Dreams, horoscopes, and tokens guided their days. Among the cases in point, a woman became confrontational when a man sneezed in her pathway. She returned to her home stating, 'Bad luck'. A taxi operator stubbed his left big toe, then parked his vehicle with the same claim. A black cat ran half way across the street before an oncoming vehicle; the bus swirled out of control. Failing to admit that he was trying to avoid the deep pot hole or even hitting the cat, the driver left the passengers stranded where it began. He claimed obeah. Green lizards, black cats or mongoose that ran close to people's paths meant an omen.

In providing reassurance of warding off bad luck, the reader man, in whom they sought for protection, luck and charm, sold them tangible symbols, thus giving them a sense of unlimited power, and then told them all that their lives were worth. In him, they claimed to experience complete deliverance. Others, out of a sense of despondency, were dependent upon him, so they chose to follow him to remain free. The dumb, the deaf, the crippled and the insane, in ones, twos, and threes, on foot and by the busloads, arrived. Eyes remained focused on the heavy traffic that arrived and departed from the church yard.

The fenced church yard carried a flowery and antiseptic fetid scent, an odour emitting basil, sulphur, myrrh and Jeyes Fluid. Jeyes is a disinfectant liquid known for its various usages, and in this case, it was used to ward off duppies. But there was nothing strange and terrifying around to brand the prophetic man as an obeah man. No skulls, vials, conch shells, fowl feathers, dead animals, horns or crystal balls were anywhere in sight. Instead, there were distinct items, but their meanings or purposes were unclear. There was a large rectangular table draped with a burnt-out red cloth. On top of the table were containers filled with water, tilley lamps, cream sodas, coconuts, crotons, a Bible, basils and burning incense. Next to the table stood an open container of water.

Inside the wooden hostel where the patrons remained for healing recovery was plain and clean. The hardwood floor was waxed with polish and the vents in the ceilings were high enough to catch the circulating mixed air. Each tiny square-shaped room had an ill-fitted cross marked with black charcoal on the ajar doors. An antique table and a makeshift board bed jammed on one side of the room. On the table was an opened Bible marked on Psalm 34 verse 3, a lamp, and note paper. The latrine and the kitchen were outside. There was no electricity, no battery radio, and except that it seemed like the perfect rehabilitation centre for troubled souls.

The reader man had a general panacea and prescription. When he hinted at their problems and anticipated something of the sort, he gave them a bath and protective trinkets. First, he looked at them disapprovingly without commenting, then made a deep disturbing groan. After which, he reached for a pencil from his head wrap and a sheet of paper from his trousers' pocket, then jotted something illegible to other eyes. The people falling in line before him were singing and dancing to the beat of drums and waving their healing fees at the same time. Then, he would spin them around three times before placing his hands upon their heads and foreheads, blessing and anointing them with 'holy water' and 'holy oil'.

The interval of prayers turned into the spewing of words, in a dialect that was not familiar to anyone but himself. Then suddenly, the people sprawled on the floor, snorting, scratching, shaking vigorously when the spirit seemed to come upon them. Loud, agonised, animated, excruciating groans and moans followed. It seemed as if some strange mysterious occurrence was taking place. It was as if something was coming out from one being to the next, or the reader- man was beating 'sin and hell' out of them. And in a rebuking voice, he would shush them; then a lapsed period of quietness ensued. Then came the clanging of cymbals, then singing and back to the drumming. Eventually, he motioned them to one of his members who gave them water to drink from a bucket inside the kitchen.

After what seemed like a period of extended agony and taunts or exorcism, the members would return to their homes 'cleansed and anointed'. And, somehow, an unusual scent always lingered with them. They looked like new converts, and their luminant faces would bear an expectant look of gratitude, contentment and redemption. Exit trinkets marked their dismissal. Their heads were usually heavily wrapped in a red cloth. They brandished candles, New Testament Bibles, guard rings, handkerchiefs, spirited oils, and such more that seemed to assure their protection and an assumption that they had paid more.

Patrons were effusive with adulation towards his efficiency, experience and discernment. They claimed that he communicated with the dead and gave them an account of their past lives. Their experience, they claimed, felt like something that could not be explained by any natural means, and his intentions were never evil because he used medicine and prayers to rid them of sickness and omen.

But not everyone shared the same thoughts about the healer man. Many whispers surfaced, claiming that he had betrayed their trust. The way about him was, for the most part, deceitful. Under the pretext of knowing, he probed into their lives; then he gave them a summation of their own testimony. But the truth was, accusations meant nothing to him. He, himself, referred to his-self, as God's anointed. His mission, as he claimed, was to eradicate evil and avengers; he healed the sick and prayed for backsliders.

On a Friday night before he began his healing spree, he would stop and take a shot of rum close to the place of worship. However, before he put the harsh liquor to his head, he would sprinkle a tiny dot on the ground, pour a small amount in his hand, rub his face and drink the remaining amount. Feeling satisfied, he emitted an 'Aah' sound. After this ritual, his strides were different. It was as if he was stepping on hot bricks. His disciples near to him would have seen his actions and smelled the rum on him. But who were they that he should have been mindful of, and who were they to judge the self-righteous unorthodox preacher? Nothing was to be said. His deportment was a reminder of the chorus:

The Lord knows I'm drinking and running around
And He don't need your loud mouth informing the town
The Lord knows I'm sinning and sinning ain't right
But me and the Good Lord's gonna have us a good talk
Later tonight

'The Lord Knows I'm Drinking' Cal Smith

18

While the reader man had a discerning eye, the villagers had an un-curtailed habit of nosiness. So far too, gossiping was a way of life for the village commoners. News always spread like wildfire and exaggerated opinions and hearsays were rampant. At times, all kinds of stories circulated that precluded the facts. As such, their tongue would speak only what their minds conceived. Even blind persons utilised their fool-proof eardrum to participate in the backbiting and slandering.

But there was one known fact about the village: there were no secrets. Indeed, it was small that it would be quite reasonable for everyone to know each other and each other's business. Chronicles of all residents were public; their political leanings, religious affiliations, professional accomplishments, literacy levels, from whence they came and why they came.

And with all probable causes, the natives felt impelled to assert their status and authority over every newcomer. Within the spirit of nosy gestures, newcomers were carefully watched. Even in the twilight hours, there were movements beneath dark paths as watchful surveillance eyes moved swiftly like mongooses. Flashlights and bottle torches, and binoculars by day, aided the onlookers. They stood guard at gates or on the street. They looped and lurked in the cane fields and in the bushes.

Of all the village lawyers and police, there was one whom never gave up duty. He was awfully inquisitive, and he seemed to have eyes that never slumbered; his prying eyes turned him into an investigator. Each newcomer was asked a barrage of incisive and interrogative questions: "Where you from? Where you going? Who you related to? Where you staying? When last you been home?"

The villagers were shrewd in questioning, but giving directions was like a story-telling, blended and twisted as a corkscrew. But never was the description less true. Accompanied with heavy usages of adjectives and prepositions in giving direction, a stranger simply needed a ton load of patience and unplugged ears. A bus load of varying groups of people alighted from a vehicle at the Crossroads: boys, girls, middle-aged men and women. Some tiny, some tall, and the others in between in size and height. Except for the children, they looked weary, battered and frail; all appearing to be absent in mind, body, and spirit. One full-sized woman was as breathless as a horse and could hardly walk. She was clutching on to her mid-section and holding tightly to the other woman's waist. They wanted to find the prominent African church yard. They were told:

"Walk towards the crossroads, then you will see a green shop on the left, pass the shop, then you will see two lanes, take the right one going uphill. On your way, you will see a Julie mango tree, two coconuts and two nutmeg trees; pass those; then you will run into a barbed wire fence; after you pass the wire fence, turn left onto the narrow lane; continue driving until you see a plum tree near to a yellow board house, then make a sharp right; you will see a donkey tied under a naseberry tree; an overarching guinep tree will be in front of a yard; not that one; go past it and two gates down and not far from it, there is a large building which has been converted into a church and you will see a large wooden cross towering more than twice the height of the building with three flags: red, green and blue, elevated on a bamboo pole in the open yard; a rusty zinc heavily chained, swing padlocked gate is engraved with a black cross. Knock on the gate and he will come out."

A description of the reader man was further given: He walked as though he was stepping on hot bricks; pain impaired his strides; he had a limp length discrepancy and was about four feet tall. His stately posture caused him to look two feet taller; a very bony, ageless Indian man with a rum belly. He always wore a kurta and a pair of eyeglasses, but he had blepharospasm, so his eyes twitched convulsively.

iving direction, going to church and funerals had the same storytelling dramatic effect. Funerals were like a confessional hearing. The people's inconsolable weeping and wailing interrupted the services of thanksgiving. Officiating ministers almost never had a chance to complete the comforting and reassuring traditional farewell hymns, or even utter known scripture passages appropriate for the dead, such as, *I am the Resurrection, and the life: he that believeth in me, though he were dead, yet shall he live.*

From the church to the grave side, the unrestrained weeping continued. The grief-stricken mourners wailed and tossed animatedly and hovered over caskets as if to caress the corpse. The same action was often repeated while the casket was being lowered into the vault. But perhaps, funerals were not the only place for consolation pangs of guilt or an act of penance. The same cries and theatrics were fashioned at some evangelical churches.

Religion was an essential fibre of the social life of the villagers, but the devout converts had so much theatrical ego that it made church-going resemble an enigma. The sanctimonious proselytisers of Christianity graced the churches' altars on Saturdays and Sundays, and they were always suitably dressed in the most stylish broad hats, long sleeved dresses and blouses, knee-high hosiery and closed-toe shoes, and yet made mockery of divine worship. There was a great deal of rivalry among them, each endeavouring to outdo the other. And there were other shortcomings. The self-righteous hypocrites were alcoholics. A man in his drunken stupor stumbled at the altar after receiving the Holy Eucharist, while all stares vented at him as he staggered back to the pews.

20

It was early evening, but the sun was already behind the darkened rain clouds displaying hazy rays, while the spectrum of the rainbow served as a reminder of God's promise. The movements on the street were scant. It was Sunday, the eve of an impending violent hurricane. No newcomers to the village were expected, not even the news team. Everything was at a standstill. Residents were indoors praying, planning and preparing, until a sudden arrival of a convoy alerted the villagers.

A rickety, chartered jalopy, packed as sardines in a tin, brought about thirteen people. The designated driver dropped them off and left in a hurry. The passengers were of similar size and features: tall and strapping and unrefined around the edges. The villagers later learned that among the women, six were siblings, the eldest being twenty-nine and everyone else was much younger. They appeared weary and expressionless, fashionable tasteless and dishevelled. Their clothes barely covered their hindquarters and midriff. All had extended hair, nails, and eyelashes. They had a knapsack on their backs and not a penny to their names.

Still, no one knew from whence they came and who had invited them. They came like a displaced army of ants, then ran and scattered like crabs in search of hiding. The villagers were sceptical about their motives and took an instinctual dislike of them. They believed it was a bad omen, as sand flies in the form of the ancestral spirits were buzzing and stinging like wild wasps.

In the hours between, swift and sudden changes of the clouds were evident, from grey to orange to black; the rain and the persistent winds took everything in its path. The villagers realised troubling and gloomy days, if not months, would be ahead. The hurricane had wreaked havoc identical to the one caused by the ruthless home wreckers.

The ignoble strangers turned the village's life upside down. They were expedient in implicating others and propagating inflammatory tales and making worthless promises. They passed themselves as trulls, and chose to use their bodies as their salvation in extorting money and faking pregnancies. The pregnancy scheme ran successfully, until it backfired when an authentication of DNA was a means to satisfy doubting fathers, but the begging and giving had tacitly stopped when crop season ended.

The women did not have any regard or respect for married life and were often caught up in love triangles. For not only must they survive, but it must be done at the expense of others. "Come here to drink milk, me nuh come here to count cows," came effortlessly in their minds and they acted on it accordingly. It was the worst of kin the village had ever witnessed. They were different in valour and ungrateful to kindness. They were messy, deceitful, cynical, and hostile. Unlike other women, who came to the village for economic opportunities and worked on the back breaking, neck twisting, heart wrenching cane fields, the siblings were devoid of ambition and education.

Each time the cunning, 'self-important' strangers walked by, they could not escape the shrewd eyes and lips of the natives piercing their flesh with utter disgust. It came at a time when fine words were no longer used to describe them. Referred to as 'the dirty dozen', the likeminded deplorables, knockabouts and soul-seeking wretches made more enemies in the village than the Nazi leader, Adolf Hitler. They never returned to their former hometown, for it was pointless; mission accomplished. Their lives were now far from discontent, and their bragging was not an empty boast. They had become what they had wanted to be, a mistress and a housewife, a reminder of a fairy tale ever after; an act of pity by the village men had become a lifetime of endowment. Tactics was all it took. A reminder of their character was uttered through the lyrics:

He who seeks of only vanity,
And no love for humanity,
Shall fade away, fade away.

He who checks for only wealth,
And not for his physical health,
Shall fade away, fade away.

Though some believe in diamonds and pearl,
And feel like they're on top of the world,
They shall fade away, hear what I say

'Fade Away' Junior Byles

ot all the women were avengers, cunning, manipulative and vain; some were noteworthy. In fact, not all the villagers were locals, and as unlikely as it may seem, there were three groups of women in Cane Field Paradise. There were the elites, otherwise called 'dry land tourists'.[10] They were ambitious and high minded, educated and well spoken, proper and private. They were never seen in rum bars or consumed liquor in the open. They were hardly seen except for a church or a funeral service. Their social gatherings were at their dwellings or outside of the village. Their market days were not the conventional Fridays and Saturdays. Grocery shopping was done through the side doors of grocers' shops or outside of the village. They hired the recommended people from the village as maids and handy men. Their husbands were either the bookkeepers or headman at the factory, or held other top paying jobs outside of the village.

The ladies of distinction devoted themselves entirely to their families and their in-laws. If any of them knew that their husband was having an affair, they never confronted him. Instead, they held pertinent discussions about faith

---

10. Dry land tourists – those who never travelled beyond land.

and relationships from Biblical passages, and thus affirming their faith in forgiveness:

Wherefore they are no more twain, but one flesh. What therefore God hath joined together, let not man put asunder.

Matthew 19:6, Bible, King James Version

With all lowliness and meekness, with longsuffering, forbearing one another in love; Endeavouring to keep the unity of the Spirit in the bond of peace.

Ephesians 4:2-3, Bible, King James Version

The second group of women were the 'mothers of invention'. Their potential was limitless. When circumstances confronted them, they used their survival instincts to make a decent living. They became unlicensed midwives, counsellors, teachers, entrepreneurs, herbalists; from the leaves to the flower, from the bark to the root of plants, herbs were liquefied and prescribed as medicines to aid in curing sickness and disease. They made jewellery and confectionaries and sold them from door to door, or sometimes they travelled outside the village and did likewise. Others ran errands for the factory workers.

They were thoughtful and talented and were determined to beautify themselves at the same time. They straightened their hair with iron combs or Jefferies' cream, and they intuitively knew how to salvage the last drop of cream to straighten a few hairs. They used natural nail polish to coat their gold-plated jewelleries to avoid them stripping. They added furniture thinners in evaporated nail polish to get every bit of content from the bottle and the brush to polish their nails; then, used the same thinner to remove nail polish from their nails. The women hand-made their clothes, from beautifully embroidered pieces to crochet tops. The ones who were not favoured with a 'desirable' figure – such as big wide hips and a small waist – enhanced their shoulders with shoulder pads, their breasts with wire-rimmed brassieres and their derrières with layering garments.

The third group of women were like the 'bar flies'. They were never seen anywhere else except at a bar. They consumed liquor like a distillery and were always drunker than a sailor. Their breath stank of stale alcohol and their voices sounded gruff. They never held a job. They had problems in terms of credibility because of carelessness and irresponsibility, so they begged like a blind person to satisfy their lifestyles.

22

The women were homogenous in terms of cleanliness. Domestic chores were meticulously done, and even the most ramshackle homes where the tiles or wooden floors were falling apart were polished and shined as bright as a diamond. They threw 'pardner'[11] and bought their necessary things, but often the houses had more furniture than they could possibly fit, and thus resembled a gift shop. Large and small stuffed toys occupied the spaces for beds, chairs and settees. Windows were draped with flowery curtains, and creepers and vines were suspended from the windowsills seemingly as if Gothel[12] had a possible gateway inside of the house.

On dining tables, buffets, break-fronts and whatnots, crochet pieces were placed with vases filled with assortments of artificial flowers along with figurines of birds and animals. Every space on the walls was occupied with grocery shop calendars of past and present years, and

---

11. Pardner – a savings partnership where each member of the group contributes an agreed amount (a 'hand') into the fund. One individual is entrusted with managing the money (the 'banker'). Each week, one member of the group receives the total amount in the fund (the 'draw').

12. Gothel – Sorceress from the Brothers Grimm fairytale, Rapunzel. She is known for uttering the iconic lines: "Rapunzel, Rapunzel, let down your hair, that I may climb thy golden stair."

scriptural quotes of protective Psalms. Psalm 23, Psalm 27, Psalm 46, Psalm 91 were hot sale for makers, vendors, and customers alike. Hanging tape measures and nailed horseshoes were on the door ledge of many of the homes. Mats and carpets lay at every door corner. And as tiny and cramped as the living quarters were, everything was stacked and neatly put away as if they were labelled. Yards were immaculately trimmed, and the front and back of tiny land spaces surrounded by sticks and barbed wire fencing were choked up with flowering plants in old chamber pots, dented pans, and painted tyres.

The line of sectional housing for the estate workers was encompassed by acres of sugarcane rows and limestone roads. The lodgings were modestly designed with box cable roofs and single floors. They were equally adjacent to each other, but all lodgings were not equal. Ordinary labourers' lodgings were simpler than wage workers and often had more occupants.

A single cramped one floor building, which rested on a stone foundation, housed transient cane cutters who came from everywhere else except the village. The complex was crowded, noisy, unkempt, poorly furnished and not air-conditioned. Rickety antique chairs and bunk beds were lined along the oblong hall with machetes, cigarettes, empty liquor bottles, radios, stacks of audio cassettes and pieces of clothing tossed in corners. The air inside blended the scents of soaps, perfumes, cigarettes and body odours. The overbearing scent caused the men to smoke and drink periodically. On the outside, cigarette butts and remnants of clothing littered the grass. Wire hangers bent into serving antennas sprouted all around the rafters of the building, with maddening discordant sounds of music emitting at the same time.

The yellowish-greenish-brownish sand-dashed wooden multi-complex building was another set of lodgings that housed field and factory staff. Some of the sectional housing units had two rooms – an inside bathroom and a kitchen – while others had one room with shared outside kitchen and latrine; all had a tiny veranda with secure bolted doors and windows.

The third set of lodgings was for management and bookkeepers. Their loggings were private, detached, larger, spacious, and fenced. The interior of the homes was comfortably furnished and spaced. The lodging had a living quarter for housekeepers, covered garage and an expansive yard space. Most of these lodgings were on a rise, and so the residents had the luxury of enjoying the incessant cool winds cutting across the rustling cane leaves. In contrast to the crisp clean air, the closely aligned roadside barracks fronting and nearing the factory, the residents had to endure the dust that the wind whipped into their homes like maddening dust storms and tainted the building like a coat of paint. At the same time, the exhaust fumes and rumbling noises from the heavy-duty vehicles shook the homes like earth tremors, while canes which fell from tractors, trailers and trucks littered the walk way.

23

There were no other places where employees showed more pride and loyalty in their work as they did at the sugar estate. They offered their superior skills, time, and talent on all junctures. Others spent their whole life working at the estate. In return, they expected nothing but fair compensation. But when their livelihood had been threatened, they had to react.

The workers were desperate for solutions, but still, it was too much scepticism and distrust between the union and the factory's barons. The workers were, however, steadfast as a tortoise and fierce like a lion, and with such fiery determination, they waged an insurrection. Their hostile, anxious voices resounded through the morning sun, followed with sparkles and glitters that grazed the cane fields.

The sudden turn of events was alarming. The military arrested people from off the streets with fierce brutality and hostility. There could be only one answer in the people's mind. Someone had betrayed them. The ill-defined days of disillusion, pain and fear rocked the rural village, and after the wretches had left the village, the estate employees were compensated and the villagers continued to relive the good ole days.

'Never again!' was the dominant emotion expressed in the village. And never could the villagers have imagined that their legacy would come tumbling down. It was not easy to grapple with the changes, and many a time, they wept at such a predicament. A heartbroken realisation came upon the village; the memory was imbued with regret, and the hurt felt like punishment. But there was nothing more they could do after making their supplication. The villagers had in the past exemplified godly qualities of charity, fellowship, and devotion, and there were, among them, people of remarkable faith, and whose faith was their assurance of prophecy fulfilled. But the people had to bring themselves in such instances of truth that it had nothing to do with God's vexation, as they have been reminded in the book of Ecclesiastes: "To everything there is a season, and a time to every purpose under heaven."

24

Remember Garvey say,
Remember weh the righteous man say,
Time a go dread ya,
Everybody a go run deh
...
I need a roof over my head,
...
And bread on my table

'I Need a Roof' Mighty Diamonds

I t is hard to imagine a time not so long ago when the village was all its worth. Never a vacant mind. Never a dull moment. There were always events and things to do. There was no other place like it. Today, there is little evidence to tell what some of the places and landmarks were known for. A generation had come to know more than ninety years of operation of the factory, which had a marked influence on the cultural heritage and landscape of the village.

There is, however, another aspect of truth that is clearly marked in the centre of the village. From a distance, a towering angular building sits idle on an expansive acre of land that would be otherwise useful for a new development. Unfortunately, a new generation would not have had any reminiscence other than beholding a hideous ramshackle building worn with age, grey and tinted from dust, emblazoned with peeling posters of events in and around the village, and its roofless top with sunlight and rain coming through the opening. But the iconic building in its former glory, the grand Apollo theatre, represented the pride and prestige of the natives. The sternly built community theatre, with high ventilated windows and wide doors, had attracted prominent performers and filmmakers in the past. Still, the theatre had been long deemed inoperable, but nothing compares to what had been taken from them: the dear beloved sugar factory.

The factory has met an unenviable demise. What used to be a source of light and life has become an idle symbol enclosed with wire fencing and padlocked gates. The huge, rustic zinc and dimly illuminated factory seemingly belongs in a different place and time. It shows nothing of its former usage. The long drawn out echoes of the carchi have been silenced and the famed factory is frozen into lifelessness.

The estate's immobile and abandoned trailers and tractors balancing on deflated tires are wreathed by shrubs on the premises. The reservoir that was used to wash canes is detained with murky water and becomes a breeding ground for mosquitoes. The workers' dwellings have long been demolished. Grass and weeds as thick as a blanket cover the columns that used to support these structures. Oxidation and corrosion have penetrated the remains of pipelines, and water columns remain sagged in the earth as if shaken by the passage of an earthquake. The few remaining canes have been overrun with vines and shrubs.

The changes are noteworthy. No summary can reclaim the wails of dismay nor outdo the acts of injustice. There is no easy answer. Everything is strange and different. Normality is far from normal. There is nothing to gain, nothing but stagnation. It is the truth about the scene of the once prestigious village; there are broken boards, plywood and zinc sheets barricading ruined buildings and now see a shelter for displaced squatters. Other buildings are draped with overgrown vines, twigs have broken windows and missing doors and have become a breeding habitat for untamed rats and nocturnal birds. Bulbs are missing from lampposts and standpipes have remained, but with no running water. Street signs have faded with traces of missing letters. Trails and shortcuts are bordered by overgrown trees and shrubs, and gravelly roads deepened with potholes have become the main cause of blown out tires and even broken feet. Nothing cushions your step and no shoemakers are around to repair your shoes.

The days and nights pass like an eclipse. As the sun falls behind the Blue Mountains, and night descends on the evening, the movements become still. Like birds on their roost, the residents are already confined to their shelters. The place is as quiet as a church mouse; not even the sound of nocturnal insects is audible from the bushy distance.

During the daytime, people walk the streets anxiously, but there is no place to go and nothing to do. Nothing to encourage the mind; nothing to discuss or debate. No one is under the ackee tree, sitting or standing or playing Ludo or dominoes or crown and anchor. No one bothers to stop the children and ask them what they learn at school. No resources are left to sustain them in spirit. The people greet each other with a nod and a disgruntled dismissal. There are no handshakes or fist bumps. The tension is 'as heavy as lead' and as sticky as cotton candy.

There is acute evidence of hardship, and the peoples' dignity and self-worth have been greatly impaired. The people are unemployable. There are no jobs in and around the villages; it is the time, of all others, that moral anguish is felt. The recompense for their employment was not a fortune of either land or cattle. There is nothing else left in reserve, not even a quattie or even an extra farthing to try their hands at gambling. A simple necessity to survive is through farming and bartering.

Small shops with poor workmanship line front yards. The tiers in the shops that remain open are half stacked. Everyone is selling just about the same items: cigarettes, sodas, crackers, and sardines, and the shopkeepers are struggling to keep things afloat. Customers come, but leave in a hurry with small grocery bags for needed items to cook for the hour. Money is lacking, so they are thrifty with their spending. The iconic Chiney man's grocery shop is lock, stock and barrel. Uncle Blass, the famous jerk man, is dead. The Credit Union, the library and the trade union office are long gone, and nothing seems left of them now. The space in the crossroads widens with emptiness; while the scent of rum and sugar dissipate with the hue of sorrow and solitude.

* * * * *

The exhaustion of life and inconsistencies has taken its toll, and like the tide, the woman's majesty has been ebbed away; she could no longer right the wrongs around her. She listened but could not speak. Her forthright voice dwindled; face covered with wrinkles and hair with greys. She was old, frail and bed ridden. Her glossy eyes affixed to the ceiling of her home in which she once reigned as a queen. The finest hour of death could arrive in a day or two, but she waited on the grandson she had loved and cared for all her life. The spirit would then return to her place of origin, Fairy Prospect, where saints and angels once tread.

She would probably sing, dance and chat with her ancestors.
But between times, her beloved grandson had announced:
"There is a death in paradise; the lights are extinguished.
The village matriarch is dead. The village is dead!"

> *By the rivers of Babylon*
> *Where we sat down*
> *And there we wept*
> *When we remembered Zion*
> *...*
> *But the wicked carried us away in captivity*
> *Required from us a song*
> *How can we sing King Alpha song in a strange*
> *land?*
> *...*
> *So let the words of our mouth*
> *And the meditation of our heart*
> *Be acceptable in Thy sight, oh Far I*
>
> 'Rivers of Babylon' The Melodians

The Thoughts of You

The thoughts of you pulsate my heart
like the rhythm of drums my ancestors pounded
when they were given the walk of freedom

The thoughts of you echo in my ears
like the sound of the abeng the Maroons blew
when they defeated the British in Accompong
 village

The thoughts of you will reign in my heart
it is the feeling of joy and reward
freedom from shackles, hate and despair
freedom to walk without restraint

The thoughts of you will reign in my heart
it is the impression you made from the start
Mother of colour, honour and valour
you touch the life of people you encounter
Your work on Earth is an indelible treasure
in the hearts that love you forever!

Georgia Brown